Based on the best-selling keyboard method *by Kenneth Baker.*

THE COMPLETE KEYBOARD PLAYER

21st Century Love Son

G000045283

Wise Publications
part of The Music Sales Group
London/New York/Paris/Sydney/Copenhagen/Berlin/Madrid/Tokyo

Published by
Wise Publications
14-15 Berners Street, London W1T 3LJ, UK.

Exclusive Distributors:
Music Sales Limited
Distribution Centre, Newmarket Road,
Bury St Edmunds, Suffolk IP33 3YB, UK.
Music Sales Pty Limited
120 Rothschild Avenue, Rosebery, NSW 2018, Australia.

This book © Copyright 2007 Wise Publications,
a division of Music Sales Limited.
Order No. AM988768
ISBN 13: 978-1-84609-854-3
ISBN 10: 1-84609-854-8

Compiled by Nick Crispin.
Music arranged by Paul Honey.
Music processed by Paul Ewers Music Design.
Edited by Rachel Payne.
Cover photograph courtesy of London Features International.
Printed in the EU.

Your Guarantee of Quality
As publishers, we strive to produce every book
to the highest commercial standards.
This book has been carefully designed to minimise awkward
page turns and to make playing from it a real pleasure.
Particular care has been given to specifying acid-free, neutral-sized paper
made from pulps which have not been elemental chlorine bleached.
This pulp is from farmed sustainable forests and was produced with special
regard for the environment. Throughout, the printing and binding have been
planned to ensure a sturdy, attractive publication which should give years of enjoyment.
If your copy fails to meet our high standards, please inform us and
we will gladly replace it.

www.musicsales.com

Master Chord Chart

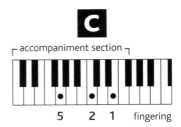

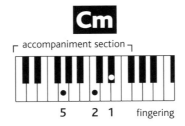

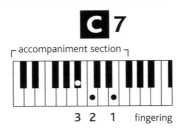

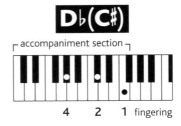

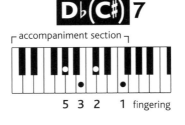

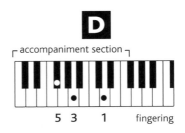

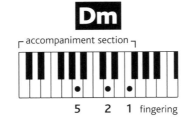

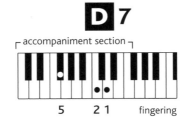

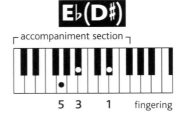

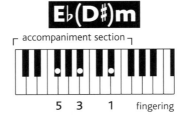

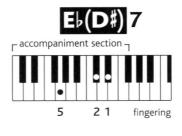

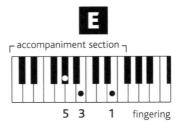

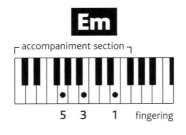

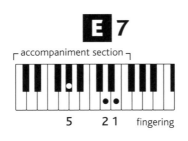

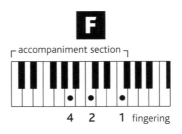

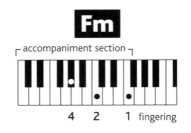

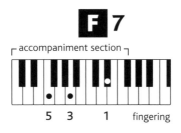

Master Chord Chart

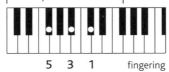

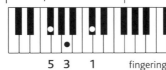

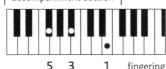

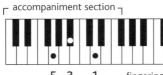

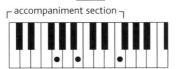

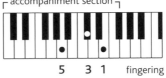

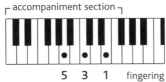

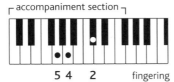

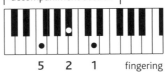

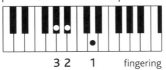

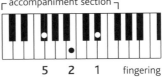

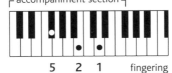

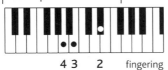

Behind These Hazel Eyes

Words & Music by Kelly Clarkson, Martin Sandberg & Lukasz Gottwald

Voice: **Accoustic guitar**
Rhythm: **8th beat**
Tempo: ♩ = 90

Seems like just yes-ter-day you were a part of me. I used to stand so tall, I

used to be so strong. Your arms a-round me tight, ev-'ry-thing it felt so right, __

un-break-a-ble, like no-thing could go wrong. Now I can't breathe, __ no,

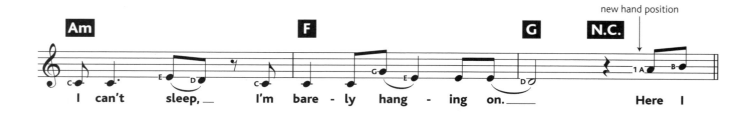

I can't sleep, __ I'm bare-ly hang-ing on. ____ Here I

am once a - gain, I'm torn in - to pie - ces; can't de - ny it, can't pre - tend, just

thought you were the one. Bro - ken up, deep in side, but you won't get to see the tears I

cry be - hind these ha - zel eyes. Here I am once a - gain, I'm

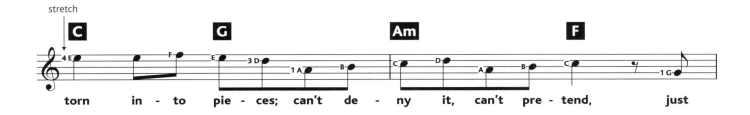

torn in - to pie - ces; can't de - ny it, can't pre - tend, just

thought you were the one. Bro - ken up, deep in side, but you won't get to see the tears I

cry be - hind these ha - zel eyes.

Born To Make You Happy

Words & Music by Andreas Carlsson & Kristian Lundin

Voice: **Electric piano**
Rhythm: **Pop**
Tempo: ♩ = 78

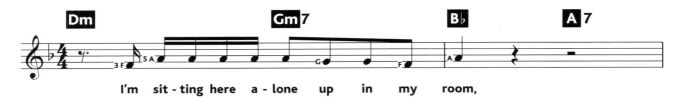

I'm sit - ting here a - lone up in my room,

and think - ing 'bout the times that we've been through, oh my love.

I'm look - ing at a pic - ture in my hand, try - ing my best to un - der -

- stand. I real - ly want to know what we did wrong with a love that felt so

strong. _____ If on - ly you were here to -

night,   I know that we could make it

right.   I don't know how to live with-out your love, I was born to make you hap - py.

'Cause you're the on - ly one with-in my heart, I was born to make you hap - py.

Al - ways and for - ev - er you and me, that's the way our life should

be. I don't know how to live with-out your love, I was born to make you hap-py.

Don't Know Why

Words & Music by Jesse Harris

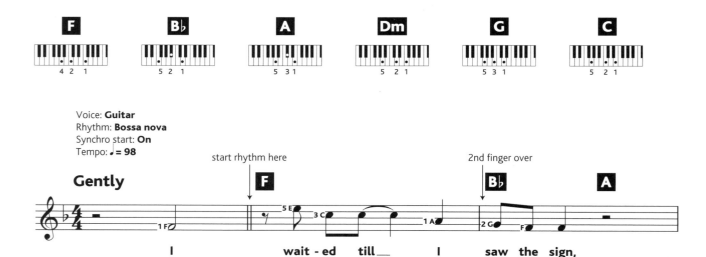

Voice: **Guitar**
Rhythm: **Bossa nova**
Synchro start: **On**
Tempo: ♩ = 98

Gently

I wait-ed till___ I saw the sign,

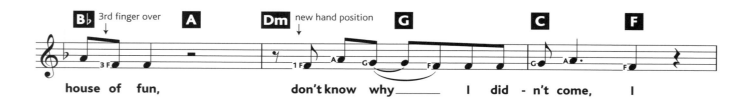

don't know why___ I did-n't come. I left you by___ the

house of fun, don't know why___ I did-n't come, I

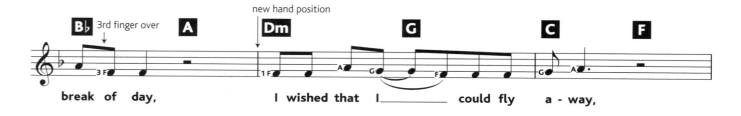

don't know why___ I did-n't come. When I saw___ the

break of day, I wished that I___ could fly a-way,

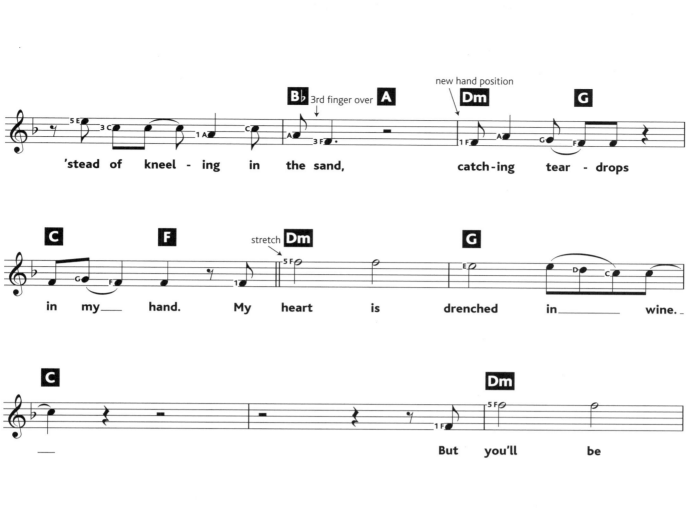

'stead of kneel - ing in the sand, catch-ing tear - drops

in my___ hand. My heart is drenched in___ wine.___

___ But you'll be

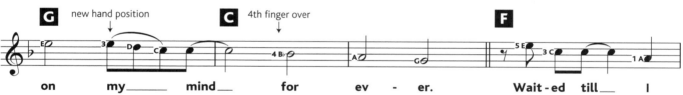

on my___ mind___ for ev - er. Wait-ed till___ I

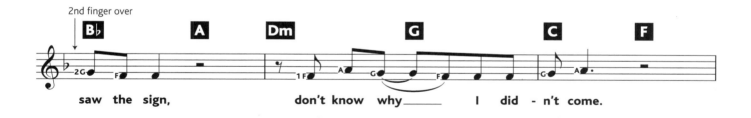

saw the sign, don't know why___ I did - n't come.

I left you by___ the house of fun, don't know why___ I did -

-n't come, I don't know why___ I did - n't come.

Evergreen

Words & Music by Jorgen Elofsson, Per Magnusson & David Kreuger

mo - ment___ and make it last for - ev - er. I'm gon - na give my

heart a - way and pray we'll stay to - ge - ther. 'Cause you're the one good

rea - son,___ you're the on - ly girl___ that I need, 'cause you're more

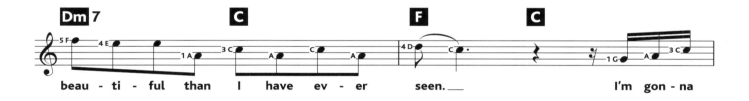

beau - ti - ful than I have ev - er seen.___ I'm gon - na

stretch

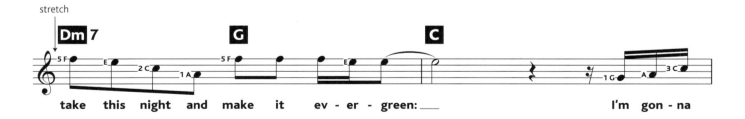

take this night and make it ev - er - green:___ I'm gon - na

stretch

stop rhythm here

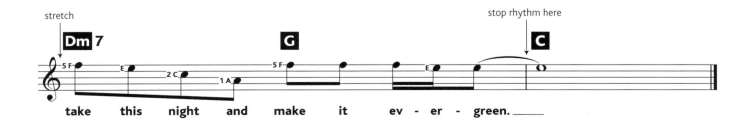

take this night and make it ev - er - green.___

Everybody's Changing

Words & Music by Tim Rice-Oxley, Tom Chaplin & Richard Hughes

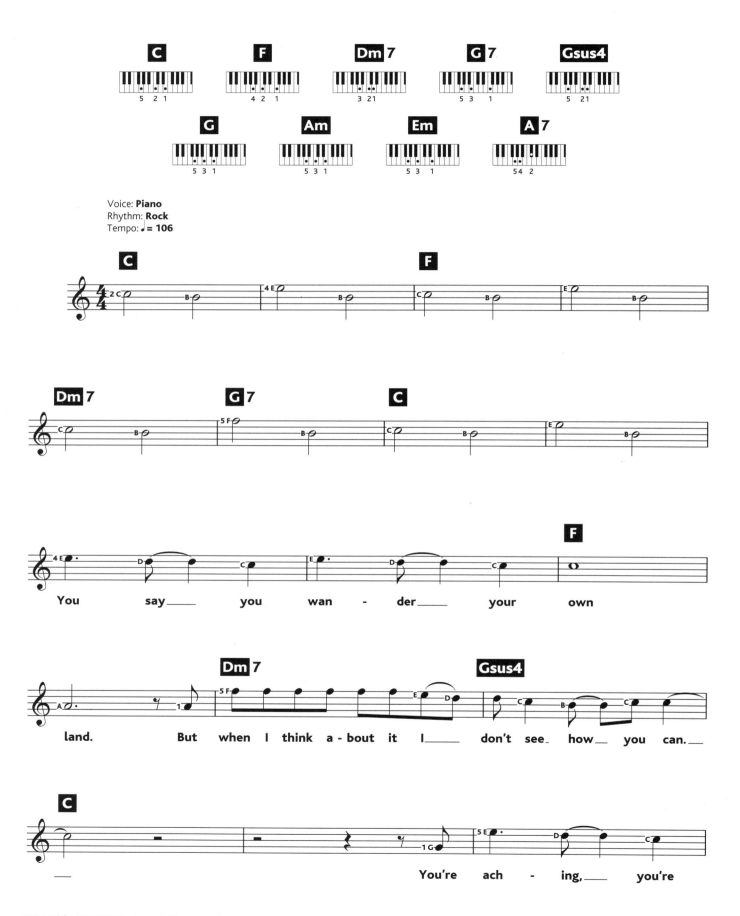

Voice: **Piano**
Rhythm: **Rock**
Tempo: ♩ = 106

You say___ you wan - der___ your own land. But when I think a - bout it I___ don't see_ how_ you can.

You're ach - ing,___ you're

break - ing____ and I can see the pain in your eyes._____ Says

ev -'ry - bo-dy's chang-ing and_ I don't know why.____

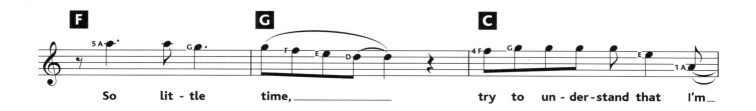

So lit - tle time,_____ try to un - der-stand that I'm_

_____ tryin' to make a move_ just to stay in the game, I'm

tryin' to stay a - wake____ and re - mem - ber my name but

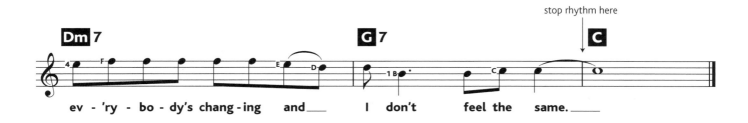

ev - 'ry - bo - dy's chang - ing and____ I don't feel the same.____

15

Feel

Words & Music by Robbie Williams & Guy Chambers

Voice: **Alto saxophone**
Rhythm: **Rock**
Tempo: ♩ = 90

Come and hold my hand,

I wan-na con-tact the liv-ing.   Not sure I un-der-

- stand   this role I've been giv - en.

I sit and talk to God,   and he just laughs at my

plans. ___   My head speaks a lan - guage

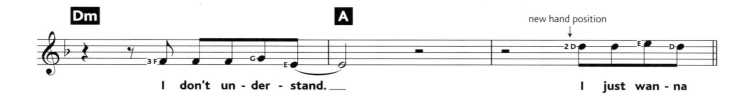

I don't un - der - stand. ___   I just wan - na

feel ___   real ___ love, ___   feel the home that I live ___ in.

'Cause I got too much life   run - ning through my veins,   go - ing to waste. _

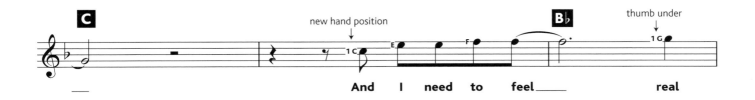

___   And I need to feel ___   real

love and a life ev - er af - ter. ___   I can - not give it up,

I can - not give it up. ___

Hurt

Words & Music by Christina Aguilera, Linda Perry & Mark Ronson

Voice: **Alto saxophone**
Rhythm: **8th beat**
Tempo: ♩ = 66

Seems like it was yes - ter - day when I saw your face,

you told me how proud____ you were, but I walked a - way.____

If on - ly I knew what I know to - day:

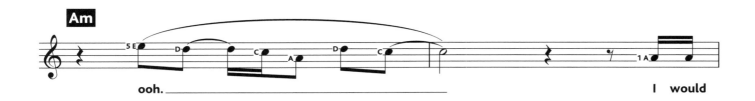

ooh.____ I would

hold you in my arms, I would take the pain____ a - way,

thank you for all you've done,_____ for - give all your mis - takes._ There's

no-thing I would-n't do_____ to hear your voice_ a - gain. Some -

-times I want_ to call you, but I know you won't be there._

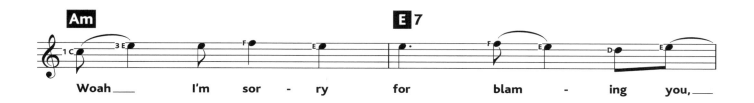

Woah_____ I'm sor - ry for blam - ing you,_

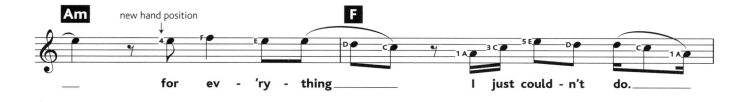

_ for ev - 'ry - thing_____ I just could - n't do._

And I've hurt_ my - self_____ by hurt - ing you.

I Want Love

Words & Music by Elton John & Bernie Taupin

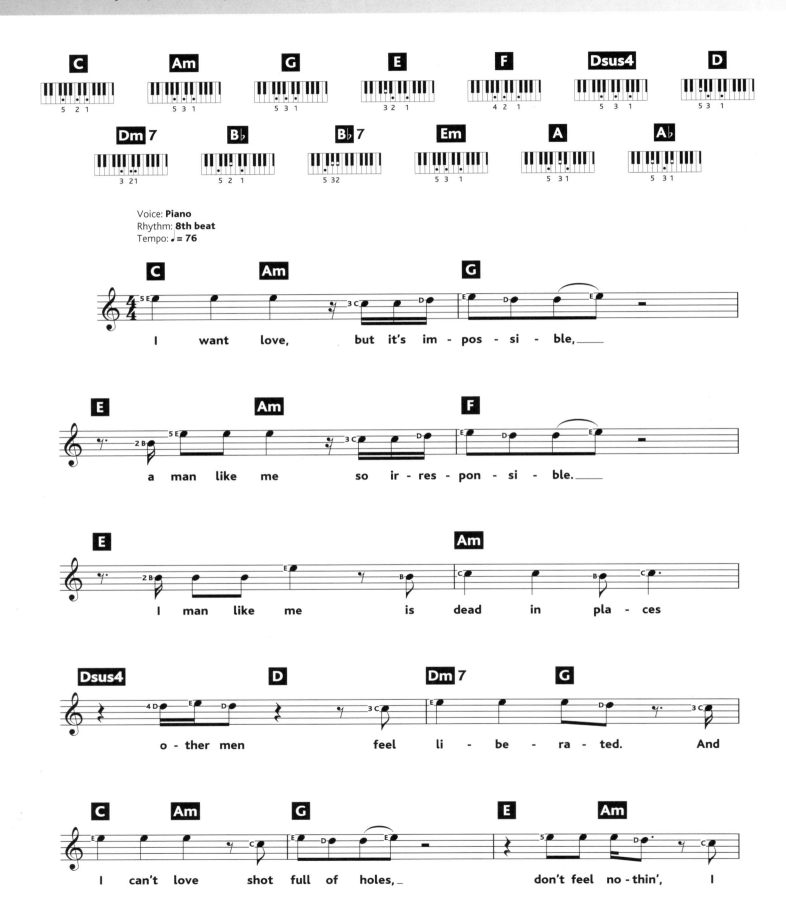

Voice: **Piano**
Rhythm: **8th beat**
Tempo: ♩ = 76

just feel cold. __ Don't feel no - thing, __ just old scars

tough-en-ing up a - round my __ heart. __ But I want love,

just a dif-fer-ent kind, __ I want love, won't break me down, __ won't

break me up, __ won't fence me in, __ I wan-na love that don't mean a thing, __ and that's the

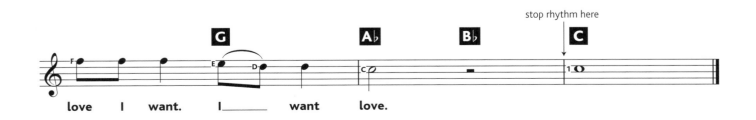

love I want. I __ want love.

If Tomorrow Never Comes

Words & Music by Garth Brooks & Kent Blazy

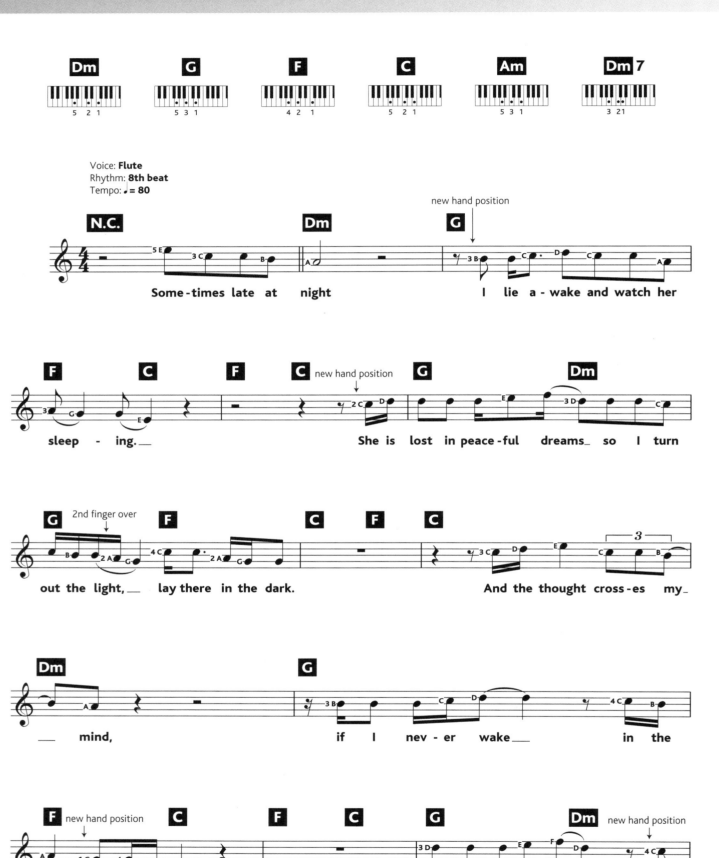

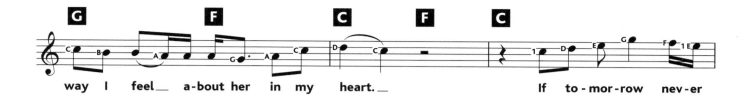

way I feel___ a-bout her in my heart. ___   If to-mor-row nev-er

comes   will she know how_ much I love her? ___

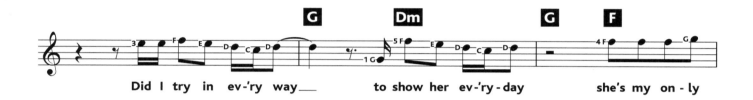

Did I try in ev-'ry way___ to show her ev-'ry-day she's my on-ly

one? _____ And if my time on earth_ were through, _

she must face this world with-out me.   Is the love I gave her in the past

gon-na be e-nough to last if to-mo-row_ nev-er comes? _____

If You're Not The One

Words & Music by Daniel Bedingfield

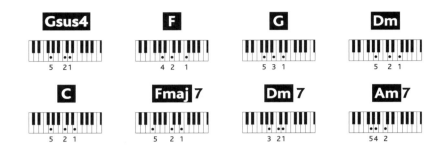

Voice: **Flute**
Rhythm: **8th beat**
Tempo: ♩ = 60

If you're not the one, then why does my soul feel glad to-day? If

you're not the one, then why does my hand fit yours this way? If

you're not the one, then why does your heart re-turn my call? If

you are not mine, would I have the strength to stand at all?

I nev-er know what the fu-ture brings but I know you're here with me now, We'll make it

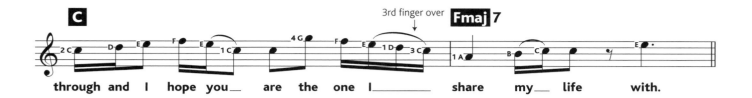

through and I hope you_ are the one I_____ share my_ life with.

I don't wan-na run a - way but I can't take it, I don't un - der -

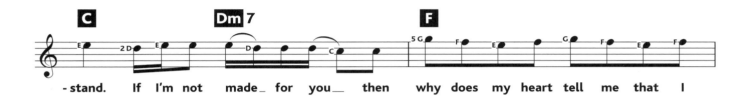

- stand. If I'm not made_ for you_ then why does my heart tell me that I

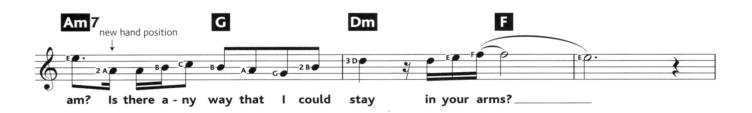

am? Is there a - ny way that I could stay in your arms?_____

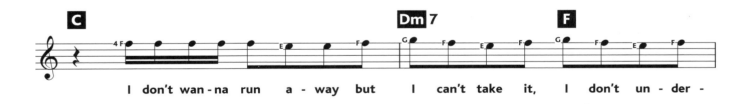

I don't wan-na run a - way but I can't take it, I don't un - der -

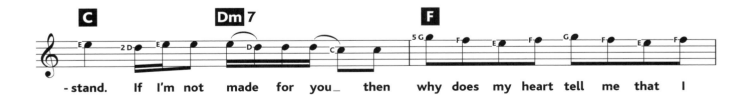

- stand. If I'm not made for you_ then why does my heart tell me that I

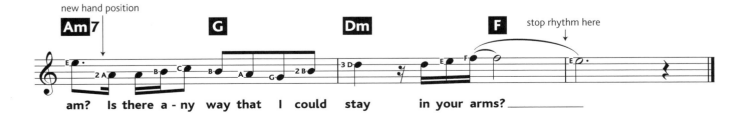

am? Is there a - ny way that I could stay in your arms?_____

I'm With You

Words & Music by Avril Lavigne, Lauren Christy, Scott Spock & Graham Edwards

Voice: **Saxophone**
Rhythm: **6/8**
Tempo: ♩. = **70**

I'm stand-ing on the bridge, I'm wait-ing in the dark. I

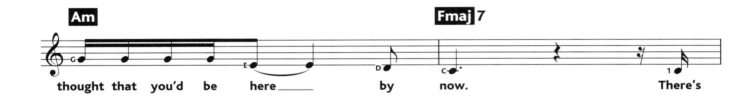

thought that you'd be here ____ by now. There's

no - thing but the rain, no foot-steps on the ground. I'm

lis - ten - ing but there's ____ no sound.

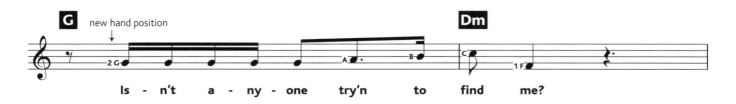

Is - n't a - ny - one try'n to find me?

Won't some-bo - dy come take me home? It's a

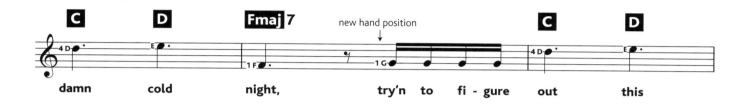

damn cold night, try'n to fi - gure out this

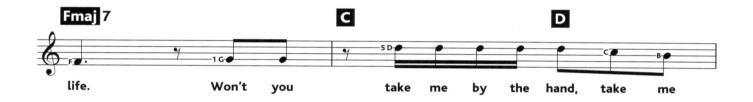

life. Won't you take me by the hand, take me

some - where new. I don't know who you are but

I, I'm with you. I'm with

you, _____ I'm with you, _____

27

In My Place

Words & Music By Guy Berryman, Chris Martin, Jon Buckland & Will Champion

Voice: **Electric guitar**
Rhythm: **Slow rock**
Tempo: ♩ = 72

In my place, in my place were lines that I could-n't

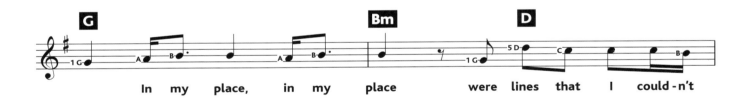

change, I was lost, oh yeah. I was lost, I was

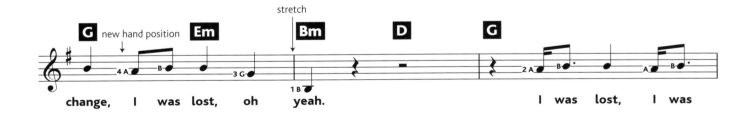

lost, crossed lines I should-n't have crossed, I was lost, oh yeah.

Yeah, _____ how long must you wait for it? Yeah, __ how

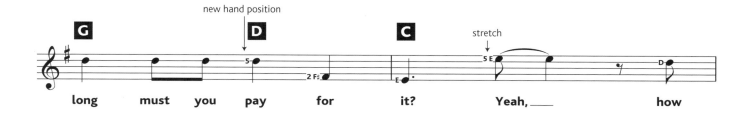

long must you pay for it? Yeah, ____ how

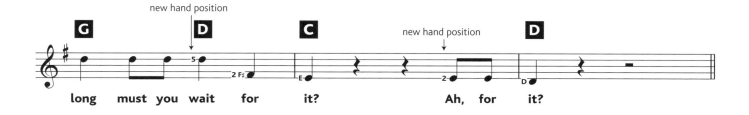

long must you wait for it? Ah, for it?

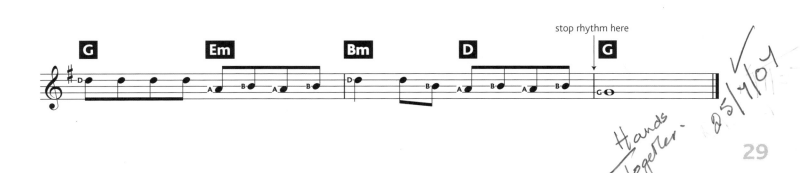

Sail Away

Words & Music by David Gray

Voice: **Flute**
Rhythm: **Ballad**
Tempo: ♩ = 60

Sail a - way with me ho - ney, I put my heart in your hands.

Sail a - way with me ho - ney now, now, now.

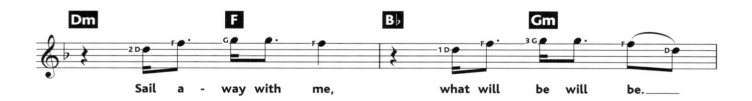

Sail a - way with me, what will be will be.

I wan - na hold you now, now,

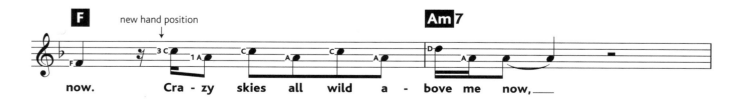

now. Cra - zy skies all wild a - bove me now,

win - ter howl - ing at my face;

and ev - 'ry - thing I hold so dear,

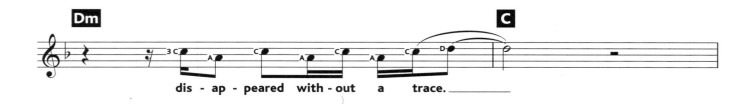

dis - ap - peared with - out a trace.

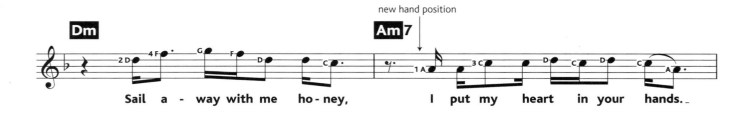

Sail a - way with me ho - ney, I put my heart in your hands.

Sail a - way with me ho - ney now, now, now.

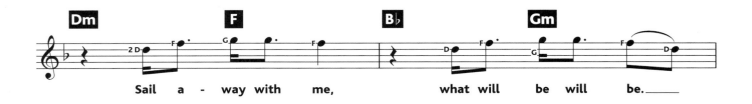

Sail a - way with me, what will be will be.

I wan - na hold you now, now, now.

She Will Be Loved

Words & Music by Adam Levine, James Valentine, Jesse Carmichael, Mickey Madden & Ryan Dusick

Voice: **Clarinet**
Rhythm: **8th beat**
Tempo: ♩ = 98

more. ___   I don't mind spend-ing   e - ve - ry   day ___

out on your cor-ner in the pour-ing rain. ___   Look for the girl with the

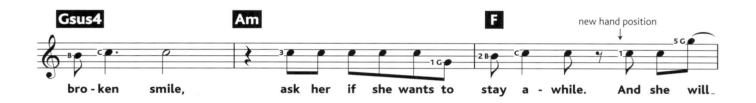

bro-ken   smile,   ask her if she wants to   stay a - while.   And she will ___

new hand position

___   be loved, ___   and she will ___   be loved. ___

_____ And she will ___   be loved, ___   and she will ___

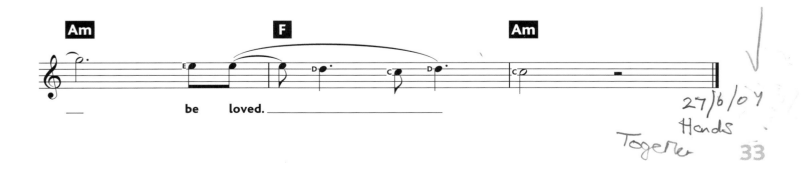

___   be loved. _____

27/6/04
Hands
Togethe

33

Songbird

Words & Music by Liam Gallagher

Voice: **Piano**
Rhythm: **Bright rock**
Tempo: ♩ = 128

Talk-ing to the song-birds yes-ter-day, threw me to a

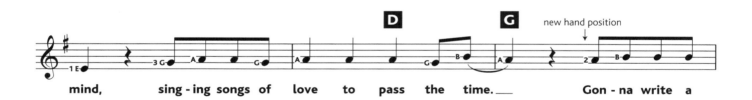

place not far a-way. She's a lit-tle pi-lot in my

mind, sing-ing songs of love to pass the time.___ Gon-na write a

song so she can see, give her all the love she gives to

me. Talk of bet-ter days that have yet to come. I've nev-er felt this

love from a - ny - one.＿＿ She's not a - ny - one.＿

＿＿ She's not a - ny - one.＿＿＿＿＿＿

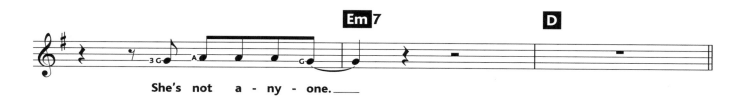

She's not a - ny - one.＿＿

new hand position   new hand position

Gon - na write a song so she can see, give her all the

love she gives to me. Talk of bet - ter days that have yet to

stop rhythm here

come. I've nev - er felt this love from a - ny - one.＿＿

Unintended

Words & Music by Matthew Bellamy

Voice: **Piano**
Rhythm: **Soft rock**
Tempo: ♩ = 66

You could be my un - in - tend - ed choice to live my

life ex - tend - ed. You could be the one I'll al - ways

love. You could be the

one who list - ens to my deep - est in - qui - si - tions,

you could be the one I'll al - ways love.

I'll be there as soon as I can,

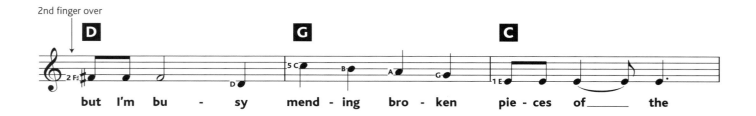

but I'm bu - sy mend - ing bro - ken pie - ces of _____ the

life I had be - fore. _____

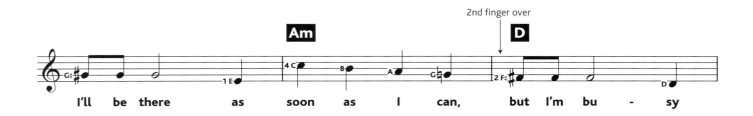

I'll be there as soon as I can, but I'm bu - sy

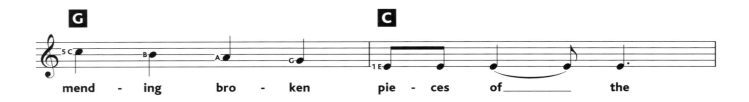

mend - ing bro - ken pie - ces of _____ the

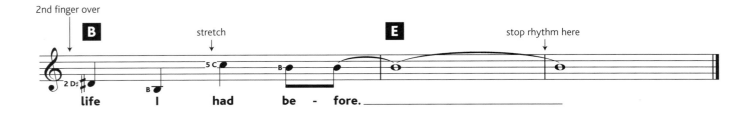

life I had be - fore. _____

You Raise Me Up

Words & Music by Rolf Lovland & Brendan Graham

Voice: **Alto saxophone**
Rhythm: **Soft rock**
Tempo: ♩ = **64**

When I am down_ and oh,_ my soul so wea-ry,___ when trou-bles

come_____ and my_ heart bur-dened be, then I am

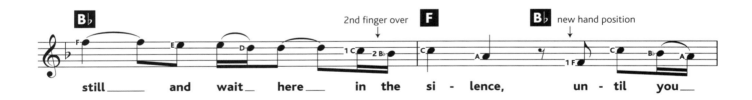

still_____ and wait_ here___ in the si-lence, un-til you_

come_____ and sit a-while_ with me. You raise me

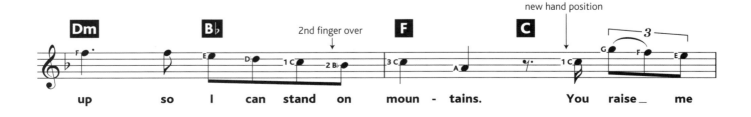

up so I can stand on moun-tains. You raise_ me

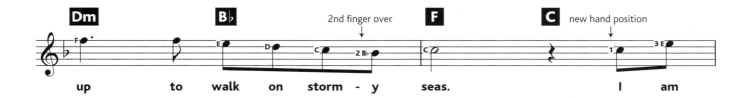

up   to   walk   on   storm - y   seas.   I   am

strong   when   I___ am   on___ your shoul - ders.___ You raise__ me

up   to   more__ than I____ can   be.   You raise   me

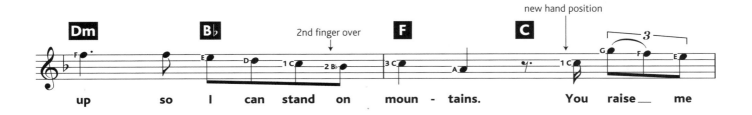

up   so   I   can   stand   on   moun - tains.   You raise__ me

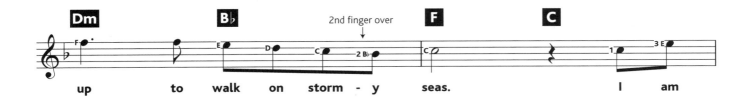

up   to   walk   on   storm - y   seas.   I   am

strong   when   I___ am   on___ your shoul - ders.___ You raise__ me

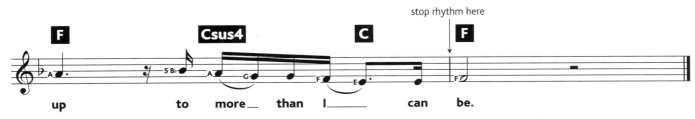

up   to   more__ than I____ can   be.

1 2 3 4 5 6 7 8 9